OLDMAN

⊕OLDMAN

Story and Art:
Chang Sheng

Adaptation:
Xiuying Zhang

Editor:
Austin Osueke

Published by:
eigoMANGA
PO Box 2071
San Jose, CA 95109
eigoMANGA.com

Distributed by:
SCB Distributors

Acknowledgment:
Ceilyne
David Heald
David Bobbitt
Dudley Pajela
Maura Werner
Peter Fisico

ISBN:
978-1636494265
Printed in the USA

CONTENTS

This publication reads
from right to left.

✝OLDMAN

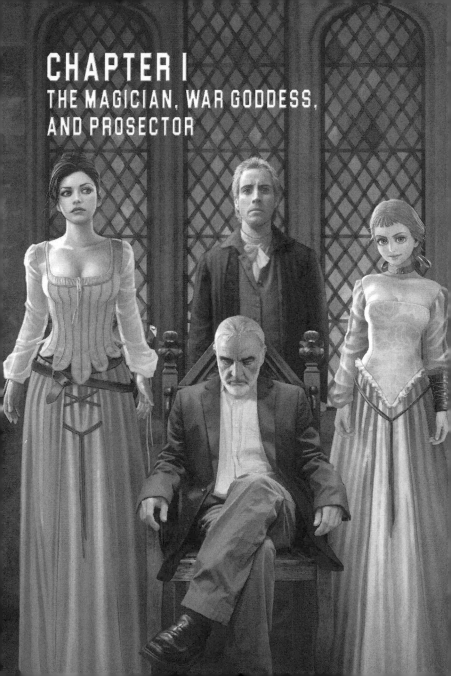

CHAPTER I
THE MAGICIAN, WAR GODDESS, AND PROSECTOR

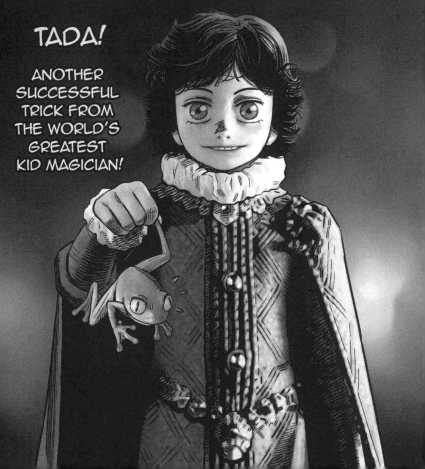

CR-
OAK!

TCH...

A FROG!?

?

MAGIC... IS ALL JUST A BIG LIE!

LISTEN WHEN I TELL YOU THIS!

MAGIC... IS ALL JUST A BIG LIE!

MY PASSION FOR MAGIC BECAME THE REASON I WAS SENTENCED TO LIFE IN PRISION.

JUST NOW... THAT MAN IS PLOTTING HIS ESCAPE.

HOW DARE HE ATTEMPT SUCH A THING?

LET ME PUT ON A MAGIC SHOW.

I'LL DO IT WITHIN THIS CELL, HERE IN THE IMPERIAL DUNGEON.

WHAT?

ON THE NIGHT OF THE FULL MOON, I'LL WALK OUT OF THIS CELL AND DISAPPEAR.

GO NOTIFY THE QUEEN. IT'S GOING BE A MAGIC SHOW AS AN EARLY NOTICE OF MY ESCAPE.

UM ...

THE NIGHT OF THE FULL MOON IS COMING SOON. I SUGGEST WE EXECUTE HIM AS PUNISH- MENT.

MAGIC ?

SHUT UP!

TCH !

MAGIC IS ALL JUST A BIG LIE.

?

JUST WHAT I'D EXPECT FROM THAT MAN. I HOPE IT WON'T BE A WASTE OF TIME.

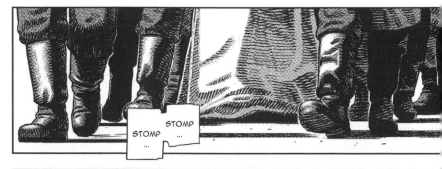

DAMN PRISONER... HOW DARE YOU NOT ACKNOW- LEDGE THE QUEEN!

MO- THER ...

...

YOU DIRTY... HOW DARE YOU ADDRESS THE QUEEN AS MOTHER? THE QUEEN IS HERE. HURRY UP AND SPEAK YOUR FILTHY NAME!

HAVE FOR- GOTTEN MY NAME? IT WAS GIVEN BY YOU.

MY DEAR BELOVED MOTHER ...

IT'S BEEN SUCH A LONG TIME SINCE WE'VE LAST MET. YOU LOOK AS YOUTHFUL AS EVER.

COMPARED TO MY OLD FACE... HOW ON EARTH DID YOU DO IT?

WHO HAVE YOU CHEATED OUT OF THEIR YOUTH?

ENOUGH! HURRY UP WITH THIS MAGIC SHOW!

MY MAGIC SHOW HAD ALREADY STARTED WHEN THE FULL MOON APPEARED.

OF COURSE. I CAN'T WAIT TO SEE THE LOOK ON YOUR FACE AFTER I'M DONE WIITH MY SHOW.

EH?

FOOL! HOW CAN YOU ESCAPE WHEN WE'RE ALL WATCHING YOU?

SPIRITS ...

...CAN'T BE CONFINED BY THESE STEEL BARS.

!

YOU
...

STOP
RIGHT
THERE
!!

!

THIS
IS...

MOTHER... NO, I SHOULD ADDRESS YOU AS THE UNAGING QUEEN.

TELL EVERYONE HOW YOU BECAME THE UNAGING QUEEN BY DECEITFUL WAYS.

YOU FILTHY GHOST !!

ONE DAY YOU'LL PAY FOR YOUR CRIMES !!

I AM THE QUEEN! NO ONE IS TO STAND OR BE SEATED AT THE SAME LEVEL AS ME !!

LOWER YOUR HEAD !!

YAAH !!

HA ...

HE VAN- ISHED !!

HUFF ... HUFF ...

HE... HE'S GONE ?

HOLD ON! THAT'S ...

HOW ON EARTH DID HE GET OUT?

HURRY, OPEN THE DOOR !!

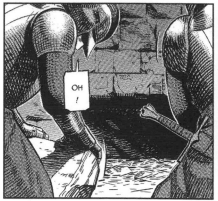

OH !

SOME-ONE WAS DIGGING HERE!

IF YOU CAN'T CATCH HIM, YOU WILL BE EXECUTED!

SEIZE HIM IMMEDIATELY!

THERE'S MOAT WITHIN THE CASTLE. HE WON'T ESCAPE.

MAGIC...

...IS JUST AN ACT PUT ON TO TRICK PEOPLE.

I TRICKED ALL OF THEM.

I MADE THEM BELIEVE THAT I HAD ALREADY LEFT THE CELL.

AND NOW... THE STEEL DOOR HAS BEEN LEFT OPEN IN THE MIDST OF THEIR CONFUSION.

THERE'S ANOTHER PERSON CONFINED IN AN EVEN DEEPER CELL WITHIN THE DUNGEON...

THAT'S THE ONLY REASON WHY I'M STILL HERE.

I NEED TO TAKE SOMEONE ALONG WITH ME.

THAT OTHER PERSON ALSO NEEDS TO SEEK VENGEANCE.

CLICK

WHO'S THERE ?

THERE WAS ONCE A WARRIOR GODDESS ON THE BATTLEFIELD OF THE GREAT REBELLION. REBECCA IS HER NAME.

SHE HAD HER LIMBS SEVERED, AND WAS THROWN IN THE IMPERIAL DUNGEON.

I'M HERE TO TAKE YOU OUT OF THIS PLACE.

BUT IT DOESN'T HAVE TO BE THIS WAY AS LONG AS YOU KEPT THE WARRIOR SPIRIT.

YOUR FATE WAS TO HAVE YOUR LIMBS SEVERED OFF, AND LEFT TO ROT IN THIS DUNGEON.

FOR A WARRIOR LIKE YOU THIS IS A FATE WORST THAN DEATH.

HA ...

HA HA...

OLD-MAN ...

YOU'RE TALKING NONSENSE.

WHO THE HELL ARE YOU?

BILLY
OLDMAN.

HUH
?

YOU'RE JUST
A CRAZY
OLD GEEZER!

I'M AS GOOD
AS DEAD.

WHAT GOOD
WILL IT BE IF I
WERE TO GO
ON LIVING?

HUFF
...
WHAT-
EVER
!

SINCE YOU CAN'T MOVE THEN I'LL JUST TAKE IT AS A YES.

FRANKLY, IF WE DON'T LEAVE NOW THEN IT'LL BE TOO LATE.

?

LET'S GO!

BITE

HOW DARE YOU INSULT ME BECAUSE I DON'T HAVE ANY LIMBS!!

AYAH!!

I HOPE YOU DON'T REGRET THIS!

DOES THIS MEAN WE'RE ALLIES NOW?

HA HA... I KNOW THIS PLACE BETTER THAN ANYONE.

DON'T TELL ME YOU INTEND TO WALK OUT OF THE PALACE WITH AN AMPUTEE ON YOUR BACK.

GEEZER, SAY THAT AGAIN AND I'LL BITE YOUR EAR OFF.

OOH! THIS IS... I'M JUST AN OLD MAN, BUT...

YOUR BODY TRULY... HAS QUITE A FEEL!

BOYS WILL BE BOYS, MY ASS!! YOU BASTARD!! GOD WILL SURELY PUNISH YOU!!

HAHA... BOYS WILL BE BOYS! AND THIS IS MY CHURCH TO EAT, DRINK, AND BE MERRY!

EH...

UM?

WHAT A SWEET PUNISH- MENT!

AHA HA...

AYAH!!

EVERYONE, LISTEN UP!

A FELON'S ESCAPED TONIGHT. THE QUEEN HAS DECREED THAT EVERY CIVILIAN IS SUBJECT TO SEARCH!

THIS PLACE STINKS LIKE HELL!

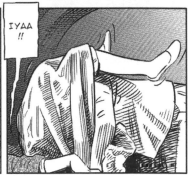

IYAA!!

ARE YOU THE ONE THEY CALL... DOCTOR VINCENT?

WHERE ARE MY MANNERS?

FUGITIVE?

OR ARE YOU THE GENIUS ARTIST?

THE SCIENTIST?

YOU'RE A MAN OF MANY TITLES.

YOU'RE SOMEONE WHO'S WELL KNOWN FOR HIS INFATUATION WITH THE HUMAN BODY A PROSECTOR.

A HU-MAN BODY...

SHIT...

AH... THAT'S RIGHT... BUT TO BE HONEST, I WALKED THROUGH THE WRONG DOOR, SO...

...PRO-SECTOR?

... MUST BE IRRE-SISTABLE TO SOME-ONE LIKE YOU...

THIS
...

I CAN
BARELY
BELIEVE IT
...

A PRETTY FACE...

SHE'S A MASTER-PIECE FROM HEAVEN.

MY HEART, BODY, AND LOINS ACT AS ONE FOR HER.

PLEASE ACCEPT THIS HUMBLE SERVANT WHO ...

DESPITE NOT HAVING ANY LIMBS, SHE HAS A PERFECT BODY.

BITE

WOW...

SHE'S SO DANGE-ROUS FOR SOMEONE WITHOUT ANY LIMBS!

I KNOW THE FEELING.

WAAAAAA!!

DAMMIT, OLDMAN!

WHERE IN THE HELL DID YOU BRING ME TO?

CHAPTER 2
THE CRIMINAL WHO ESCAPED A YEAR AGO

ONE
YEAR
AFTER
THE
ESCAPE

MY MAGIC GOES BEYOND LIFE AND DEATH.

I CAN REACH THROUGH THE PAST AND FUTURE WITH EASE.

ARE YOU READY?

RST

ALLOW ME TO INTRODUCE ...

MUR- MUR

CLA- MOUR

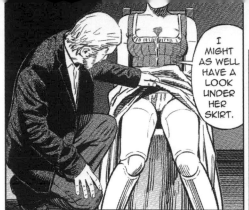

I MIGHT AS WELL HAVE A LOOK UNDER HER SKIRT.

UNFORT-UNATELY THIS DOLL WON'T MOVE WITHOUT HELP.

OH ...

CLA-MOUR

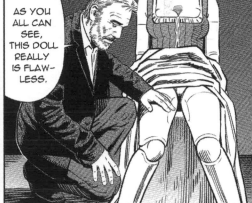

AS YOU ALL CAN SEE, THIS DOLL REALLY IS FLAW-LESS.

SMACK!

PER-VERT !

AH!

IT MOVED!

THE DOLL MOVED!

AH! HAHA!!

I REGRET THAT SHE'S SO HOSTILE, BUT THIS BEAUTY IS MY ASSISTANT FOR THE REST OF THE MAGIC SHOW!

AH... MY DEAR, TELL HIM, CAN YOU TALK?

WOW!

THE DOLL CAN MOVE!

CAN IT TALK?

THAT'S NONE OF YOUR BUSINESS.

AH...

AH...

HAHA HA...

HA HA ...

HAHA ...

HA HA...

HA HA HA ...

HEY... A DOLL SHOULD ONLY MOVE WHEN THE MAGICIAN TELLS IT.

• • • • • • •

THIS MIRROR IS SUSPENDED BY ROPES.

TAP

BUT... CAN A MIRROR LIE?

AS YOU KNOW, A MIRROR SHOWS WHATEVER IS IN FRONT OF IT...

THE WORLD INSIDE A MIRROR LOOKS SO REAL, BUT DOES IT EXIST?

AH... AS YOU CAN SEE, A MIRROR DOESN'T LIE...

UNLESS ...

THE WORLD INSIDE THE MIRROR ACTUALLY EXISTS!

WOW...

MY GOD!

AH!

WHAT?!

NEXT
...

NOW
I WILL LET
THE MAN
COME TO
THE REAL
WORLD.

COME
OUT!

WAIT A MINUTE ... LOOK AT THAT!!

HOW IS THIS POSSIBLE !? AH!!

THE MAN FROM THE MIRROR... ONE OF HIS SHOES IS DIF- FERENT!

LOOK !!

UM!

IS THIS MAGIC FAKE?

AH, HE'S RIGHT !!

WHY IS THAT ?

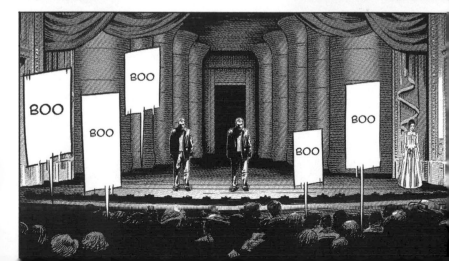

HMM
...

PULL

WHAT A DISASTER!

IT WASN'T THE MAGIC THAT WAS AT FAULT.

WE HAVE MORE SHOWS LINED UP. THEY ARE SURE TO ATTRACT A LARGER AUDIENCE.

TODAY'S OPENING SHOW WAS SUCH A BIG MISTAKE.

HOW AM I SUPPOSED TO STAY IN BUSINESS?

NO, I WON'T ALLOW IT! AND I'LL ONLY PAY HALF OF TODAY'S WAGE!

WHAT ELSE CAN YOU DO NOW? THE GREAT MAGICIAN OLDMAN IS NOTHING BUT A FRAUD!

HEY!

......

LISTEN TO ME!

WHAT ARE YOU DOING?

HUH?

...YOU ARE NOW A CURSED MAN! YOU WILL GRADUALLY GROW WEAKER, YOU WILL REMAIN IN THAT CHAIR!

THE VERY MOMENT I TOUCH YOUR FOREHEAD WITH MY FINGER...

MY GOD!!

I CAN'T MOVE MY HANDS!

I CAN'T STAND UP!!

YOU CAN'T GET UP, AND YOUR HANDS HAVE LOST THEIR STRENGHT.

LET'S GO!

WHAT KIND OF CURSE IS THIS?

HELP ME!!

DAMN IT!!

DO YOU EVEN WANT HALF YOUR WAGE!?

HUH?

HEY! WAIT A MIN-UTE!

WHEN A FINGER IS UP AGAINST YOUR FORE-HEAD!

IT'S COMMON KNOW-LEDGE!

YOU CAN'T MOVE YOUR UPPER BODY

HA...

HA...

HA...

DON'T RUN !!

STOP !!

STOP !!

HA...

HA...

THEY'LL CATCH ME SOON!

I MUST FIND HIM!

QUICK, GRAB HER!

AH ...

IT'S JUST LIKE I SAID...

HOW CAN SOMEONE SO GIFTED PUT ON THE WRONG SHOE?

RIGHT?

MY FIELD IS ANATOMY, NOT BEING AN ENTERTAINER. HAVING ME AS A STAND-IN WAS A BIG MISTAKE!

YOU TOO ARE SAME. YOU'RE BOTH NOTHING BUT FRAUDS!

ENO-UGH!!

DON'T REMIND ME ABOUT THE SHOE!

SO YOU WON'T ADMIT TO WEARING THE WRONG SOCKS TOO?

76

AH
!!

HUH!

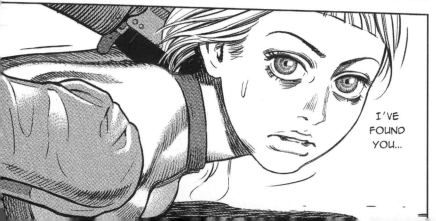

I'VE FOUND YOU...

THAT GIRL... NO!
IT CAN'T BE
POSSIBLE!

TAP

TAP

TAKE
HER
AWAY!

AHH
...

HELP ME.

UHH ...

HUH!

THAT GIRL...

WHO ARE YOU PEOPLE? IT'S BEST THAT YOU DON'T GET INVOLVED!

DO YOU KNOW THIS GIRL?

NO, WE DON'T KNOW HER.

THEY'RE PALACE GUARDS. WE CAN'T DO ANYTHING THAT WOULD GIVE AWAY OUR IDENTITY!

HEY, WE SHOULD STEAL THEIR HORSES AND USE THEM AS OUR OWN.

USE YOUR MAGIC!

SHH

....

TAKE HER AWAY!!

STOP!
LET
ME
GO!

NO
OTHER
WAY...

OLD-MAN !!

UH, SHE SAID YOUR NAME!

YOU FOOLS! **LOOK!** THEY ARE THE ONES WHO ESCAPED THE PALACE DUNGEON A YEAR AGO!

OLDMAN! I'VE SEEN YOU BEFORE!

········

EH... SHOULD WE RUN NOW?

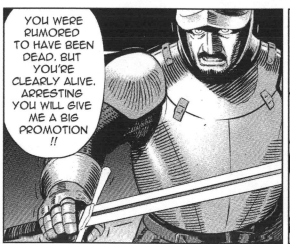

YOU WERE RUMORED TO HAVE BEEN DEAD. BUT YOU'RE CLEARLY ALIVE. ARRESTING YOU WILL GIVE ME A BIG PROMOTION!!

YOU BASTARD... I'M NOT AFRAID OF YOUR CHEAP TRICKS!

CHAPTER 3
SWITCH ON
COMBAT STANCE

CAP-
TAIN
!!

HE'S
ONLY AN
OLD MAN.
I'M MORE
THAN
ENOUGH
TO
HANDLE
HIM!

YOU'RE
COMING WITH
US, OLDMAN!
DEAD OR
ALIVE!

NO!
DON'T
KILL
HIM!

?

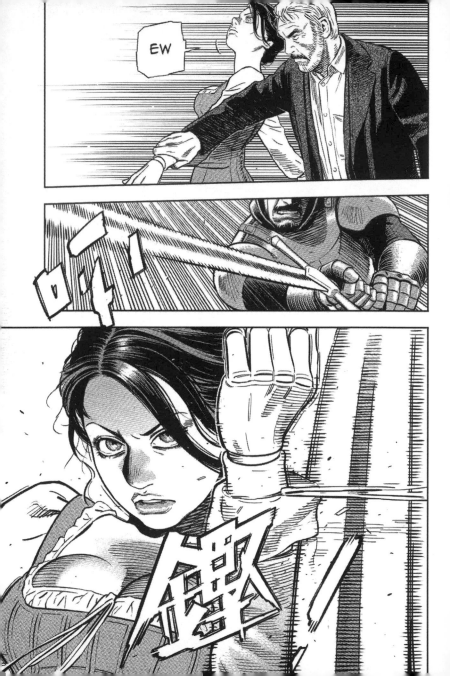

WHAT THE HELL? DO YOU WANT TO DIE! HOW DARE YOU USE ME AS YOUR SHIELD!

YOU... USED YOUR ARM TO BLOCK MY SWORD!

RING

IT WAS WRONG OF ME TO HAVE YOU AS MY ASSISTANT FOR THE SHOW. YOU'RE ONCE THE GODDESS OF WAR. WON'T YOU DEFEND US?

AAAHH, MY ARM!

DIE!!

SON OF A BITCH! TWO GROWN MEN NEED MY PRO-TECTION!!

YAAA!!

I HAVE A BAD FEELING ABOUT THIS!

KONG!

SHIT!

PING

HOW ... HOW DID IT ...

NOW... IS THE TIME TO LEAVE...

AH

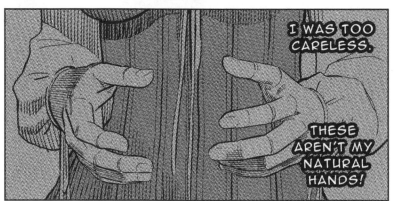
I WAS TOO CARELESS.

THESE AREN'T MY NATURAL HANDS!

MAKE YOUR PEACE YET?

SWITCH ON...

COMBAT STANCE !!

WAIT, I GOT IT!!

HEY, REB- ECCA ...!

WHAT?

EH !!

THE SWITCH'S ON THE SURFACE OF YOUR INNER THIGH!

COM- BAT STANCE ...!

WHAT THE HELL IS THAT ?

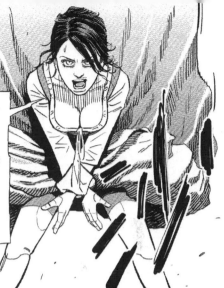

SON OF A BITCH...! WHAT KIND OF POSE ARE YOU MAKING ME DO?! WHY DID YOU PUT THE SWITCH IN SUCH A WEIRD PLACE?

YOU... WHAT ARE YOU DOING?

JUST PRESS IT DOWN!

HUH?

HEY! HAVEN'T YOU SEEN ENOUGH?

HE FLEW!

CAP- TAIN!

WOW

INSIDE YOUR LIMBS ARE EQUIPED WITH HUNDREDS OF DIFFERENT SIZED WEIGHTS. WITH THE PRECISE MOVEMENT, THE WEIGHTS COMBINED WITH SPEED CAN PRODUCE A POWERFUL FORCE.

SO STRONG!

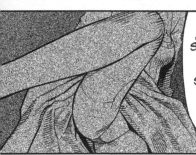

THE PLACEMENT OF THE SWITCH MAKES FOR A SHOCKING SURPRISE FOR ENEMIES IN SITUATIONS LIKE THIS. HEHEHE...

UM!

AH, YOU CAN LOWER YOUR LEG NOW. THE REST OF THE MEN ARE RUNNING FORWARD!

ARGH

!!

MASTER-PIECE!

UM, IT'S RUDE TO QUESTION MY JUDGE-MENT. THIS CREATION IS MY GREATEST ...

WAIT A MINUTE. YOU... FILLED MY LIMBS FULL OF GUN-POWDER?

YOU BETTER RUN FOR YOUR LIVES!

RELEASE ME !!

CAP-TAIN!

GEN-IUS!

TIN

OH! IT'S HEAVY ...

WAIT... I ALMOST FORGOT WE NEED THAT HORSE!

RUN!

HFFF

DOGS OF THE QUEEN...

LEAVE THE HORSE BEHIND!!

IT'S MY TIME TO SHINE..

I'M GOING TO IMPRESS THEM!

GET THE HELL OUT!!

HUFF!

HUFF

STAB

YOU... WHAT HAVE YOU DONE..?

EW

DOM

I DON'T RECALL EVER MEETING YOU BEFORE. HOW DID YOU KNOW ABOUT OLDMAN'S PRISON ESCAPE?

HA! IT WAS THE ONLY WAY.

YOU GUYS WOULD'VE STOOD BY AND LET THEM ARREST ME.

...WE'LL MURDER YOU AND DISSECT YOUR BODY! HEHEHE...

YOU BETTER TELL US THE TRUTH OR ELSE...

WHO ARE YOU? WHAT'S YOUR GOAL FOR MEETING US?

UGHH...

HOW SHO-ULD I SAY IT?

WOULD ANYONE BELIEVE IT?

NO... NO ONE WOULD ACTUALLY BELIEVE THE TRUTH...

WHO AM I?

WHY DIDN'T I THINK OF THIS BEFORE? WHAT NAME SHOULD I USE..?

UGH...

EWW!!

YOU HAVE BEEN VISITING A PROSTITUTE !!

I'M REALLY DISA-PPOINTED IN YOU! I THOUGHT WE ARE BUDDIES. WHY WASN'T I INVITED?

HM-PF

BUT... IT'S PRETTY FUNNY! HEHE... HOW DID IT END UP LIKE THIS? UCHH...!

NO! NO! NO! I KNEW THIS ISN'T GOING TO WORK!!

EH

THAT'S RIGHT!

YOU'RE LAUGHING AND CRY-ING AT THE SAME TIME. HAVE YOU GONE NUTS?

PUFF

I AM THIS CENTURY'S MOST POWERFUL, GREATEST, AND PRETTIEST CLAIRVOYANT!!

LET ME CORRECT MYSELF! I AM SENT HERE BY THE ALMIGHTY GOD.

MUWAH HAHA! YOU REALLY ARE SOMETHING ELSE!

HEHE...

HAHA!!

YOUR GIRLFRIEND'S A TOTAL NUTCASE!

WHAT DOES THE FUTURE HOLD WHEN YOU ADD A CLAIRVOYANT TO YOUR GROUP?

AND MY GIFTS GAVE ME THE ABILITY TO FIND YOU ALL AT THIS EXACT MOMENT!

WHAT'S SO FUNNY? MY GIFTS TOLD ME EXACTLY WHO YOU GUYS ARE.

THAT... I CAN'T TELL YOU!

AH!

HEY!!

WHY DON'T YOU PREDICT WHAT HAPPENS TO US IN THE FUTURE?

HEY... YOU'RE LIKE A MYSTERY THAT WE DON'T WANT TO SOLVE!

WHAT IS YOUR NAME?

MY NAME!! SHIT!! MY NAME IS... MY NAME... MY NAME...

EH, NOT! AGAIN! YOU CAN'T COME UP WITH A LIE ON YOUR FEET!

OOOH!!

IT'S TIME... WE SHOULD GO.

THE SKY... IT'S GETTING DARK.

SURE.

HELEH! MY NAME IS HELEH!

EH? HEY, WAITA MINUTE! I GOT IT!

I CAN FORSEE THAT YOU'LL LET POOR LITTLE ME... WHO WAS SENT FROM HEAVEN... THE PRETTIEST CLAIRVOYANT TO JOIN YOU! I'VE NEVER BEEN WRONG!

WAIT!

JUST GO HOME, HELEH!

WHAT
DID
YOU
SAY?

I SWEAR
TO GOD...
THE MAN
WE ENCOUN-
TERED WAS
OLDMAN.

...
OLDMAN
!

I DON'T KNOW HOW HE'S STILL ALIVE, BUT HE'S THE ESCAPEE FROM A YEAR AGO...

IT CAN'T BE WRONG!

THEN WHY DID SOMEONE TELL ME... THAT MAN WAS DEAD?

।।।।।।।

* AND MY YOUTH IS STAR- TING TO FADE AS WELL!

WHERE DID HE HIDE FOR A WHOLE YEAR?

EET
...

THERE WAS ANOTHER MAN AND WOMAN WITH HIM.

YOU MEN ARE ...

...THE PALACE GUARDS. JUST HOW WAS ONE OLD MAN ABLE TO DEFEAT YOU?

SHE WAS AS STRONG AS STEEL. SHE WAS AS FLEEING AS A GHOST. AND SHE DEFEATED US WITH EASE.

HER LIMBS MAKE HER LOOK LIKE A MANNEQUIN, BUT SHE WAS ABLE TO ATTACK US WITH INHUMAN POWER!

REBECCA!? I'M PRETTY SURE THAT I HAD HER ARMS AND LEGS CHOPPED OFF.

A WOMAN ...

USELESS!! GET OUT OF MY SIGHT!! I'LL HAVE YOUR HEADS IF YOU MOVE ANY SLOWER!

MAR- CELLO CERVINI !!

YOU'RE A USELESS ADVISOR! WHY IS OLDMAN STILL ALIVE, AND WHY ARE YOU NOT DEAD?

MOVE !!

SUMMON HAMMER TO THE PALACE!

I NEED ELITE SOLDIERS TO DEAL WITH THIS CHAOS!

PLEASE FORGIVE ME BUT... THIS TASK IS BENEATH THE LEVEL FOR ME AND MY MEN.

DO WE REALLY NEED TO WASTE OUR ENERGY ON AN OLD TRICKSTER?

YOUR MAJESTY, OLDMAN IS ONLY AN OLD GEEZER. IS THERE REALLY A NEED TO SUMMON ME?

HAMMER, I NEED YOU AND YOUR MEN FOR AN URGENT MISSION.

AND THERE IS ANOTHER PERSON IN OLDMAN'S GROUP THAT WILL PEAK YOUR INTEREST.

YOU AND YOUR ARMY BELONG TO ME. I EXPECT ABSOLUTE LOYATY!

TZZ...

YOU DEFEATED HER ONCE. THE GODDESS OF WAR, REBECCA.

HAVE YOU FORGOTTEN HER?

REBECCA!

OH...

HOW COULD I EVER FORGET?

YES. I'M NOT A FOOL.

MY QUEEN, I'M AFRAID THAT I WON'T BE ABLE TO BRING THEM BACK ALIVE.

ARE YOU SCARED?

IT SEEMS THAT SHE STILL HAS A WARRIOR'S SPIRIT DESPITE LOSING ALL OF HER LIMBS.

TELL ME, JUST WHAT KIND OF REWARD DO YOU WANT FOR YOU TO BRING OLDMAN BACK ALIVE..?

GO!

HAHAHA... I HOPE YOU WON'T DISAPPOINT ME!

MY OWN LAND!

DON'T ASK SO MANY QUESTIONS! GO!

HIS LIFE IS MINE!!

WHAT IS OLDMAN TO YOU? WHY DO YOU WANT HIM ALIVE, YOUR MAJESTY?

CHAPTER 4
ORIGIN

YOU
MEN
ARE
...

YOU DON'T KNOW, EH? THAT MAKES THINGS DIFFICULT FOR US. WE WERE TASKED TO FIND THEM IMMEDIATELY. LET ME THINK.

I... REALLY DON'T KNOW THE WHERE-ABOUTS OF OLDMAN'S GROUP.

I ACTUALLY LOVE A GOOD MAGIC SHOW, AND YOU'RE THIS THEATRE'S OWNER RIGHT?

WHY DON'T YOU SHOW US A LITTLE MAGIC TRICK?

THAT'S RIGHT!

THEN ...

HURRY UP AND GIVE US A SHOW.

IF I DON'T LIKE IT, YOU'LL DIE.

WHAT ?

I WILL BEGIN!

HMM ...

?

YOUR BODY WILL BEGIN TO FEEL POWERLESS AFTER I LAY MY INDEX FINGER ON YOUR FOREHEAD.

THIS IS... THE MAGIC TRICK...

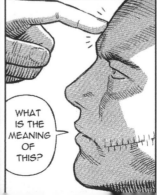

WHAT IS THE MEANING OF THIS?

... CAN'T EVEN STAND ...

STRENGHT IS FLEE- ING FROM YOUR LIMBS UNTIL YOU ...

ZHE

WHAT KIND OF MAGIC TRICK IS THIS?

LOOKS LIKE I WILL HAVE TO KILL YOU AFTER ALL!

ARE YOU JUST BRAVE OR ARE YOU REALLY THIS STUPID?

AAHH !!!

PLEASE DON'T KILL ME! I KNOW WHERE OLDMAN AND THE OTHERS ARE!

NO...

THEY'RE LIVING IN THE ABANDONED MANOR, SOUTHWEST OF THE CITY!

SO YOU DO KNOW! THIS WOULD'VE GONE SO MUCH SMOOTHER IF YOU SPOKE SOONER.

WHAT?

THANK YOU. NOW WHY DON'T YOU..?

RUN FOR YOUR LIFE!

IT'S A PITY BUT...

BURN THIS PLACE DOWN TO THE GROUND!

PFFF, THIS MAGIC TRICK WAS SUCH A DISAPPOINTMENT!

THIS PLACE IS ON FIRE !!

FIRE !!

BOOM

OLD-MAN !!

AAHHH !!

IS SHE THAT TIRED?

YOU... WENT TO SLEEP BEFORE FINISHING YOUR SENTENCE?

UM?

JUST WHAT KIND OF DANGER?

DANGER IS...

OH MY GOD!! I SLEPT THROUGH IT!!

I HAVE TO WARN THEM!

DANGER IS... OUCH!

WHAT TIME IS IT? SHIT! IT'S ALREADY MORNING!!

KNG

BREAK-FAST IS SERVED!!

MOVE OUT OF THE WAY!!

THIS PAN IS USELESS!!

CHA

AAHH !!

KENG

WHE-
RE
...

...DID HE COME FROM?

TAKE A CLOSE LOOK! HE'S NOT JUST ANY ORDINARY PALACE GUARD.

I DON'T NEED TO SAY SUCH NON-SENSE!

HEY, YOU FORGOT TO SHOUT "SWITCH ON COMBAT STANCE!!"

ARGH !!

HERE COMES ANO- THER!

HE'S PART OF HAMMER'S ARMY!

I'VE BEEN WAITING FOR YOU!

OFF YOU GO!!

YOU SLEPT IN THE MIDDLE OF OUR CONVERSATION!

I TOLD YOU GUYS THAT YOU'RE IN DANGER!

WHY DIDN'T YOU LISTEN!?

THEY FOUND OUR SHELTER. I'M AFRAID THAT THEY HAVE THIS PLACE SURROUNDED!!

THIS ISN'T GOOD!! ARE WE BEING TRACKED BY THE QUEEN'S SPECIAL ARMY?

IDIOT!! DON'T OPEN THE DOOR!!

WHAT ARE YOU DOING?

I CAN'T OPEN IT! WE NEED TO LEAVE NOW!!

KAKA

BLOCK THE DOOR!!

I'LL GO OUTSIDE!!

DAMN IT! WE TOLD YOU NOT TO OPEN THE DOOR!

HUH
?

BLOCK
IT!?
WITH
WHAT?

AARGH
!!

SHIT!! HE SLAMMED THE DOOR DOWN!!

WE'RE ALL OUT OF EGGS!! TRY MY SPECIALITY INSTEAD!!

I'M TRAPPED!! HEY... SOMEONE STOP HIM!! HELP!!

OH LOOK! THE PAN IS FIXED!

THE FRYING PAN'S USELESS!! TRY HITTING HIM WITH SOMETHING ELSE!!

WE'RE ALSO OUT OF FRYING PANS TOO! EAT THIS CHAIR!

DOES THIS HOUSE HAVE ANY WEAPONS BESIDES FRYING PANS AND CHAIRS!?

SAVE ME PLEASE!!

I'M SORRY, BUT MY HANDS ARE TIED. YOU'RE ON YOUR OWN!

YOU'RE SUCH A PEST!

CAN'T YOU SEE I'M TRAPPED? THERE'S NO OTHER WAY FOR ME TO GET OUT!!

BASTARD!
DON'T
CRY OUT
AGAIN!

A
GUN!

EVEN IF YOU'VE OBTAINED INHUMAN POWERS WITH YOUR NEW LIMBS, YOUR BODY STILL BLEEDS ALL THE SAME.

IS IT REALLY YOU?

REBECCA... THE GODDESS OF WAR WHO LOST HER LIMBS?

I WILL KILL YOU BEFORE YOU CAN PULL THE TRIGGER!!

TRY TO REPLACE THAT!

I WILL SHOOT BETWEEN YOUR EYES AND WATCH YOUR BRAINS SPLATTER!

ACE
!!

!?

BA!

PLAYING
CARD!?

KING!

AGAIN
!?

QUEEN!

OLDMAN, STOP IT! YOU'RE GOING TO GET REBECCA KILLED!

OLD GEEZER! WHAT ARE YOU TRYING TO DO? THIS ISN'T A CHEAP MAGIC SHOW!!

YOUR FOOLISH GAMES HAS SEALED HER FATE!

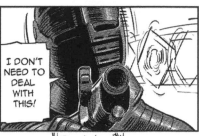

I DON'T NEED TO DEAL WITH THIS!

DIE!!

JACK!

AH
!!

PAIN

STOP
!!

ARGH
!!

FAAA

CH!

DA DA...

HE'S ESCA-PING!!

AH! HE HID THE HORSE BEHIND THE TREES!

I'M GOING TO STOP HIM! OTHERWISE, HE'LL BRING BACK MORE SOLDIERS!!

WAIT FOR ME!

AH!

I HOPE YOU CAN OUTRUN A HORSE!

IT DOESN'T MATTER IF HE ESCAPES BECAUSE THEY ALREADY KNOW WHERE WE LIVE!

WE SHOULD JUST AND HIDE SOMEWHERE ELSE!

WHAT? WHAT ARE YOU DOING?

HUFF HUFF ...

WHERE IS HE?

THESE AREN'T FOR YOU!

YOU'D PROBABLY SHOOT THE HORSE ANYWAY!

WHAT ARE YOU DOING WITH THOSE?

SORRY, BUT I DON'T KNOW HOW TO USE THEM.

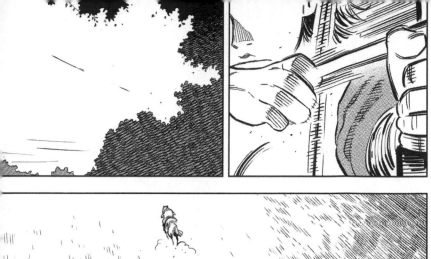

BULLS-
EYE!

AN
ARROW
!?

REBECCA STOPPED HER CHASE. SEEMS LIKE HE WAS HIT BY THE ARROW.

WHAT? DID HE GET HIT? I CAN BARELY SEE HIM. HOW DID YOU MANAGE TO LAND THE SHOT?

WHO SHOT THE ARROW?

RE-BECCA!!

LET'S GO!

OUCH! MY LEG! WAIT FOR ME!

HELEH!? YOU CAN USE A BOW!? YOU WERE AT LEAST 200 YARDS FROM HERE, AND THAT'S NO SMALL FEAT.

!

HUFF... HUFF HUFF HUFF... IT WAS HELEH.

AH! AH... HOLD ON!

I AM THE BEAUTIFUL CLAIR-VOYANT! WHY DON'T YOU TRUST ME!?

JUST WHO ARE YOU? WHAT OTHER SECRETS ARE YOU HIDDING FROM US?

FROM THE WAY YOU TALK... AND YOUR ARCHERY SKILLS... ARE YOU FROM THE PALACE?

OLD-MAN?

IS HE TAKING A BREAK UNDER THE TREE?

YOU BETTER EXPLAIN YOUR-SELF!

I MET YOU GUYS YESTER-DAY, THEN I FELL ASLEEP DURING OUR CONVER-SATION. THERE'S BARELY TIME TO EXPLAIN THINGS!!

THIS PLACE.

THIS TREE.

FATHER AND MOTHER WERE LEAVING.

IT WAS HERE... THAT I DISCOVERED THE HIDDEN SECRET. THE SECRET OF TIME... THE MEMORIES ARE ALL COMING BACK TO ME SO VIVIDLY.

I WAS WAITING UNDER THIS TREE. EVEN THOUGH I KNEW THEY WILL NEVER COME BACK FOR ME.

A SPECIFIC PART THAT COULD FULLY EXPLAIN THE REASON BEHING EVERYTHING.

NO! I SEEM TO HAVE FORGOTTEN PARTS OF MY MEMORIES.

YOU'VE MASTERED ARCHERY SINCE YOU WERE A CHILD, AM I RIGHT?

I'M OLD-MAN'S GIRL-FRIEND!

I REMEMBER SOMETHING FROM A LONG TIME AGO...

OLD-MAN! WHAT'S WRONG?

THIS PLACE... IS THE ORIGIN THAT CAUSED EVERYTHING! BUT NO MATTER WHAT I TRY, I STILL CAN'T REMEMBER A CERTAIN PART OF MY PAST.

THE ORIGIN!

IT'S BEEN ONE LONG YEAR! WHY DON'T I FEEL ANY SORT OF CAMARA-DERIE BETWEEN US?

OLDMAN! AREN'T WE ALLIES?

WHO ARE YOU? WHY DID THE QUEEN PUT YOU IN THE DUNGEON? WHY DID THE QUEEN'S SPECIAL ARMY NEED TO COME AFTER YOU? WHAT KIND OF SECRETS ARE YOU KEEPING BETWEEN YOU AND THE QUEEN? WHAT OTHER SECRETS ARE YOU HIDING FROM US?

AREN'T YOU SEEKING VENGEANCE? WHAT IS YOUR REASON?

AND NOW YOU WANT TO GO TO THE PALACE TO DIE?

WHAT'S YOUR REASON FOR RESCUING ME OUT OF THE DUNGEON?

I'M A PERSON WHO DOESN'T HAVE ANY LIMBS!

REBECCA, YOU ALREADY KNOW THAT WE DON'T HAVE THE MANPOWER TO SET OUR PLAN IN MOTION.

IF WE EXACT REVENGE IN OUR CURRENT STATE, ONLY DEATH AWAITS US ALL.

WITHOUT VENGEANCE I'M NO MORE THAN A LIVING DEAD!

I'M A LIVING DEAD WHO KEEPS ON DREAMING! NIGHT AFTER NIGHT, I HAVE NIGHTMARES ABOUT HAVING MY ARMS AND LEGS CHOPPED OFF. DO YOU THINK OF ME AS ANYTHING MORE THAN A USELESS MANNEQUIN?

IT WAS YOU WHO GAVE ME HOPE... TO COMPLETE A TASK THAT I COULD NEVER FULFILL BY MYSELF. MY ONLY GOAL IN LIFE... IS REVENGE AGAINST THE QUEEN!

IF I DON'T COME BACK BY THE AFTERNOON... YOU GUYS CAN DO AS YOU WISH!

YOU GUYS WILL KNOW THE TRUTH SOON ENOUGH. I HAVE TO GO SEE THAT PERSON, BUT NOT TO WAGE WAR.

......

YOU REALLY ARE A STUBBORN OLD GEEZER! I HOPE YOU'LL GET YOUR WISH... WALKING INTO THE LION'S DEN!

END OF VOLUME ONE